In My Humble Opinion

KNOCK KNOCK®
LOS ANGELES, CALIFORNIA

Created, published, and distributed by Knock Knock
11111 Jefferson Blvd. #5167
Culver City, CA 90231
knockknockstuff.com
Knock Knock is a registered trademark of Knock Knock LLC
Inner-Truth is a registered trademark of Knock Knock LLC

ISBN: 978-1-68349-302-0
UPC: 825703-50199-5

10 9 8 7 6 5 4 3 2 1

OTHER PEOPLE ARE SO ANNOYING.

If it weren't for all those total idiots, your life would be great. After all, you're a good driver, a sensible friend, a nuanced coworker, a caring mate, and, most of all, you know how to stand in a line without cutting. Given the antics of the thronging rabble, however, "If you're not angry, you're not paying attention," as the bumper sticker says. We might all be better off if we weren't paying attention—to the tailgating jerk behind us, the woman screeching into her cell, or the waiter who thinks he's God's gift. Centuries before bumper stickers enriched our lives (and sucky commutes), eighteenth-century poet Thomas Gray famously said "Ignorance is bliss," and no doubt it's still true.

But for better or worse, you don't have the gift of oblivion. You notice every tiny irritating tic and injustice and spend your hours wondering why people are like that. And who could blame you? There's a lot to vent about these days, from the significant (war, global warming, social media "influencers") to smaller, everyday annoyances (pop songs, junk mail, overpriced coffee) to the philosophical (do humans even matter in the cosmos?). We live in congested cities, competing for resources, clogging highways, and generally rubbing up against one another. The damaging effects of such proximity have been proven: in renowned studies on the deliberate overcrowding of rats, high levels of aggression and poor health were the inevitable result.

Annoyance isn't very good for you, either. Research shows that those with high hostility levels are likely to die younger than those with low or average levels, primarily from heart disease. Anger's effects include the release of hormones adrenaline and noradrenaline, increased heart rate and blood pressure, and the movement of sugar into the bloodstream. But it also appears that we crave anger—as much as sex, food, or drugs: a Vanderbilt University study showed that aggression engages the brain's reward pathways and involves dopamine.

Experts believe that anger is generally best suppressed (not expressed), but that it can be damaging when repressed (not known or acknowledged). Journaling is thus an ideal outlet for aggression: you won't anger anyone else, and you just might work through your own anger. As Kathleen Adams, founder of the Center for Journal Therapy, puts it, journals are "79-cent therapists."

According to a widely cited study by James W. Pennebaker and Janel D. Seagal, "Writing about important personal experiences in an emotional way for as little as fifteen minutes over the course of three days brings about improvements in mental and physical health." Proven benefits include stress management, strengthened immunity, fewer doctor visits, and improvement in chronic illnesses such as asthma. "It's hard to believe," says Pennebaker, a psychology professor at the University of Texas at Austin, but "being able to put experiences into words is good for your physical health." How does this work? Some experts believe organizing experience into a narrative may be helpful. According to scholarship cited in *Newsweek*, journaling "forces us to transform the ruminations cluttering our minds into coherent stories. Writing about an experience may also dull its emotional impact." Psychologist Ira Progoff, father of the modern journaling movement, stated in 1975 that an "intensive journal process" could "draw each person's life toward wholeness at its own tempo."

To get the most out of the process, here are a few tips: experts agree that you should try to write quasi-daily, for at least five to fifteen minutes. For inspiration, famed diarist Anaïs Nin suggests asking yourself, "What feels vivid, warm, or near to you at the moment?" Don't critique your writing; just spew. Finally, choose a safe home for your journal where others won't find it.

Thomas Jefferson declared, "When angry, count ten, before you speak. If very angry, an hundred." Mark Twain advised, "When angry, count four. When very angry, swear." We say, "When angry, irritated, or bursting with humble opinions, journal."

I hate morning people. And mornings. And people.

Grumpy Cat

Why People Are Like That Today:

TODAY'S DEFINITIVE CONCLUSION ABOUT HUMANITY:

☐   ☐   ☐   ☐

The problem with the gene pool is that there is no lifeguard.

Steven Wright

DATE:

—— Why People Are Like That Today: ——

TODAY'S DEFINITIVE CONCLUSION ABOUT HUMANITY:

☐   ☐   ☐   ☐

I like sometimes for people to be afraid of me.

Indra Nooyi

DATE:

Why People Are Like That Today:

....

....

....

....

....

....

....

....

....

....

....

....

....

....

....

....

....

....

TODAY'S DEFINITIVE CONCLUSION ABOUT HUMANITY:

☐   ☐   ☐   ☐

Human beings, who are almost unique in having the ability to learn from the experience of others, are also remarkable for their apparent disinclination to do so.

Douglas Adams

Why People Are Like That Today:

....

....

....

....

....

....

....

....

....

....

....

....

....

TODAY'S DEFINITIVE CONCLUSION ABOUT HUMANITY:

☐   ☐   ☐   ☐

Every year, back Spring comes, with the nasty little birds yapping their fool heads off, and the ground all mucked up with arbutus.

Dorothy Parker

DATE:

Why People Are Like That Today:

....

....

....

....

....

....

....

....

....

....

....

....

....

....

TODAY'S DEFINITIVE CONCLUSION ABOUT HUMANITY:

☐   ☐   ☐   ☐

I'm my own
soulmate

No, I'm never
lonely

I know I'm a queen
but I don't need
no crown.

DATE:

Why People Are Like That Today:

....

....

....

....

....

....

....

....

....

....

....

....

....

TODAY'S DEFINITIVE CONCLUSION ABOUT HUMANITY:

☐   ☐   ☐   ☐

Many people would sooner die than think. In fact, they do.

Bertrand Russell

Why People Are Like That Today:

TODAY'S DEFINITIVE CONCLUSION ABOUT HUMANITY:

☐   ☐   ☐   ☐

Maybe this world is another planet's Hell.

Aldous Huxley

— Why People Are Like That Today: —

TODAY'S DEFINITIVE CONCLUSION ABOUT HUMANITY:

☐   ☐   ☐   ☐

Golden Delicious apples. Where do they get off naming their apples that? That's a little immodest, isn't it? What if I called myself "Incredibly Attractive Ellen"?

Ellen DeGeneres

DATE:

Why People Are Like That Today:

....
....
....
....
....
....
....
....
....
....
....
....

TODAY'S DEFINITIVE CONCLUSION ABOUT HUMANITY:

☐   ☐   ☐   ☐

And isn't your life extremely flat

With nothing whatever to grumble at!

W.S. Gilbert

DATE:

Why People Are Like That Today:

....

....

....

....

....

....

....

....

....

....

....

....

....

....

TODAY'S DEFINITIVE CONCLUSION ABOUT HUMANITY:

☐   ☐   ☐   ☐

People. People drag you down.

Stephen King

Why People Are Like That Today:

....

....

....

....

....

....

....

....

....

....

....

....

....

TODAY'S DEFINITIVE CONCLUSION ABOUT HUMANITY:

☐   ☐   ☐   ☐

The more humanity advances, the more it is degraded.

Gustave Flaubert

DATE:

Why People Are Like That Today:

....

....

....

....

....

....

....

....

....

....

....

....

....

TODAY'S DEFINITIVE CONCLUSION ABOUT HUMANITY:

☐   ☐   ☐   ☐

Since I no longer expect anything from mankind except madness, meanness, and mendacity; egotism, cowardice, and self-delusion, I have stopped being a misanthrope.

Irving Layton

DATE:

Why People Are Like That Today:

....

....

....

....

....

....

....

....

....

....

....

....

TODAY'S DEFINITIVE CONCLUSION ABOUT HUMANITY:

☐   ☐   ☐   ☐

I only go
out to get
me a fresh
appetite for
being alone.

Lord Byron

DATE:

Why People Are Like That Today:

....

....

....

....

....

....

....

....

....

....

....

....

TODAY'S DEFINITIVE CONCLUSION ABOUT HUMANITY:

☐   ☐   ☐   ☐

No one really listens to anyone else, and if you try it for a while you'll see why.

Mignon McLaughlin

Why People Are Like That Today:

TODAY'S DEFINITIVE CONCLUSION ABOUT HUMANITY:

☐   ☐   ☐   ☐

It's too bad that stupidity isn't painful.

Anton LaVey

Why People Are Like That Today:

....

....

....

....

....

....

....

....

....

....

....

....

TODAY'S DEFINITIVE CONCLUSION ABOUT HUMANITY:

☐   ☐   ☐   ☐

How I hate the attitude of ordinary people to life. How I loathe ordinariness! How from my soul I abhor nice simple people, with their eternal price list. It makes my blood boil.

D. H. Lawrence

DATE:

——— Why People Are Like That Today: ———

....

....

....

....

....

....

....

....

....

....

....

....

TODAY'S DEFINITIVE CONCLUSION ABOUT HUMANITY:

☐ 　　☐ 　　☐ 　　☐

I worry no matter how cynical you become, it's never enough to keep up.

Jane Wagner

Why People Are Like That Today:

TODAY'S DEFINITIVE CONCLUSION ABOUT HUMANITY:

☐   ☐   ☐   ☐

Some scientists claim that hydrogen, because it is so plentiful, is the basic building block of the universe. I dispute that. I say there is more stupidity than hydrogen, and that is the basic building block of the universe.

Frank Zappa

Why People Are Like That Today:

TODAY'S DEFINITIVE CONCLUSION ABOUT HUMANITY:

☐   ☐   ☐   ☐

Don't waste your energy trying to educate or change opinions ... Do your thing and don't care if they like it.

Tina Fey

Why People Are Like That Today:

TODAY'S DEFINITIVE CONCLUSION ABOUT HUMANITY:

☐   ☐   ☐   ☐

The chief obstacle to the progress of the human race is the human race.

Don Marquis

Why People Are Like That Today:

TODAY'S DEFINITIVE CONCLUSION ABOUT HUMANITY:

☐   ☐   ☐   ☐

"Well, if you want my opinion—"
"I don't," she said.
"I have my own."

Toni Morrison

Why People Are Like That Today:

TODAY'S DEFINITIVE CONCLUSION ABOUT HUMANITY:

☐   ☐   ☐   ☐

Cynicism is an unpleasant way of saying the truth.

Lillian Hellman

DATE:

Why People Are Like That Today:

....

....

....

....

....

....

....

....

....

....

....

....

TODAY'S DEFINITIVE CONCLUSION ABOUT HUMANITY:

☐   ☐   ☐   ☐

In nature a repulsive caterpillar turns into a lovely butterfly. But with human beings it is the other way around: a lovely butterfly turns into a repulsive caterpillar.

Anton Chekhov

Why People Are Like That Today:

TODAY'S DEFINITIVE CONCLUSION ABOUT HUMANITY:

☐   ☐   ☐

The only thing that will be remembered about my enemies after they're dead is the nasty things I've said about them.

Camille Paglia

Why People Are Like That Today:

TODAY'S DEFINITIVE CONCLUSION ABOUT HUMANITY:

□   □   □   □

A true gentleman is one who is never unintentionally rude.

Oscar Wilde

Why People Are Like That Today:

TODAY'S DEFINITIVE CONCLUSION ABOUT HUMANITY:

☐   ☐   ☐   ☐

Common sense is not so common.

 Voltaire

Why People Are Like That Today:

....

....

....

....

....

....

....

....

....

....

....

....

....

....

TODAY'S DEFINITIVE CONCLUSION ABOUT HUMANITY:

☐   ☐   ☐   ☐

Arriving late was a way of saying that your own time was more valuable than the time of the person who waited for you.

Karen Joy Fowler

Why People Are Like That Today:

TODAY'S DEFINITIVE CONCLUSION ABOUT HUMANITY:

☐   ☐   ☐   ☐

Much virtue in herbs, little in men.

Benjamin Franklin

DATE:

Why People Are Like That Today:

....

....

....

....

....

....

....

....

....

....

....

....

....

TODAY'S DEFINITIVE CONCLUSION ABOUT HUMANITY:

☐   ☐   ☐   ☐

When I think of the number of disagreeable people that I know who have gone to a better world, I am sure hell won't be so bad at all.

Mark Twain

Why People Are Like That Today:

....

....

....

....

....

....

....

....

....

....

....

....

....

TODAY'S DEFINITIVE CONCLUSION ABOUT HUMANITY:

☐   ☐   ☐   ☐

I won't smile, but I'll show you my teeth.

Halsey

DATE:

Why People Are Like That Today:

....

....

....

....

....

....

....

....

....

....

....

....

TODAY'S DEFINITIVE CONCLUSION ABOUT HUMANITY:

☐   ☐   ☐   ☐

It's raining outside and the world reeks of despair. Even my cold cereal doth taste like wormwood.

Linus (Peanuts)

DATE:

Why People Are Like That Today:

....

....

....

....

....

....

....

....

....

....

....

....

TODAY'S DEFINITIVE CONCLUSION ABOUT HUMANITY:

☐   ☐   ☐   ☐

Nobody ever lost a nickel betting against the intelligence of the American public.

P. T. Barnum

Why People Are Like That Today:

TODAY'S DEFINITIVE CONCLUSION ABOUT HUMANITY:

☐   ☐   ☐   ☐

I don't have pet peeves, I have whole kennels of irritation.

Whoopi Goldberg

Why People Are Like That Today:

TODAY'S DEFINITIVE CONCLUSION ABOUT HUMANITY:

☐   ☐   ☐   ☐

I am frequently enraged by people but I just am not great at expressing my anger, so most of it turns into a lot of stern walking around the city blasting rap into my brain.

Maya Angelou

DATE:

— Why People Are Like That Today: —

....

....

....

....

....

....

....

....

....

....

....

....

TODAY'S DEFINITIVE CONCLUSION ABOUT HUMANITY:

☐   ☐   ☐   ☐

No man lives without jostling and being jostled; in all ways he has to elbow himself through the world, giving and receiving offense.

Thomas Carlyle

DATE:

Why People Are Like That Today:

···

···

···

···

···

···

···

···

···

···

···

···

···

TODAY'S DEFINITIVE CONCLUSION ABOUT HUMANITY:

☐ 　　☐ 　　☐ 　　☐

I love humanity; but I hate people.

Edna St. Vincent Millay

DATE:

Why People Are Like That Today:

....

....

....

....

....

....

....

....

....

....

....

....

....

TODAY'S DEFINITIVE CONCLUSION ABOUT HUMANITY:

☐   ☐   ☐   ☐

Maybe the best thing would be to forget being right or wrong about people and just go along for the ride. But if you can do that—well, lucky you.

Philip Roth

Why People Are Like That Today:

TODAY'S DEFINITIVE CONCLUSION ABOUT HUMANITY:

☐   ☐   ☐   ☐

I love having every right to be as outspoken as I am, as any man would be.

Chrissy Teigen

Why People Are Like That Today:

....

....

....

....

....

....

....

....

....

....

....

TODAY'S DEFINITIVE CONCLUSION ABOUT HUMANITY:

☐   ☐   ☐   ☐

What I hear when I'm being yelled at is people caring loudly at me.

Leslie Knope (Parks and Recreation)

DATE:

Why People Are Like That Today:

....

....

....

....

....

....

....

....

....

....

....

....

....

TODAY'S DEFINITIVE CONCLUSION ABOUT HUMANITY:

☐   ☐   ☐   ☐

Just think of how stupid the average person is, and then realize that half of them are even stupider.

George Carlin

Why People Are Like That Today:

TODAY'S DEFINITIVE CONCLUSION ABOUT HUMANITY:

☐   ☐   ☐   ☐

Humanity is a pigsty, where liars, hypocrites, and the obscene in spirit congregate.

George Moore

DATE:

Why People Are Like That Today:

TODAY'S DEFINITIVE CONCLUSION ABOUT HUMANITY:

☐   ☐   ☐   ☐

Human beings cling to their delicious tyrannies, and to their exquisite nonsense . . . till death stares them in the face.

Sydney Smith

Why People Are Like That Today:

TODAY'S DEFINITIVE CONCLUSION ABOUT HUMANITY:

☐   ☐   ☐   ☐

You see men blow up all the time, and it's not a big deal. But if a woman does it, either she's crazy or she's shrill. It's like, you know what? She may just be angry.

Naomi Campbell

DATE:

Why People Are Like That Today:

....

....

....

....

....

....

....

....

....

....

....

TODAY'S DEFINITIVE CONCLUSION ABOUT HUMANITY:

☐   ☐   ☐   ☐

I love mankind . . . It's people I can't stand!

Charles M. Schulz

DATE:

Why People Are Like That Today:

....

....

....

....

....

....

....

....

....

....

....

....

TODAY'S DEFINITIVE CONCLUSION ABOUT HUMANITY:

☐   ☐   ☐   ☐

What can we know? What are we all? Poor silly half-brained things peering out at the infinite, with the aspirations of angels and the instincts of beasts.

Arthur Conan Doyle

Why People Are Like That Today:

....
....
....
....
....
....
....
....
....
....
....
....

TODAY'S DEFINITIVE CONCLUSION ABOUT HUMANITY:

☐   ☐   ☐   ☐

I am not lucky. You know what I am? I am smart, I am talented, I take advantage of the opportunities that come my way and I work really, really hard. Don't call me lucky.

Shonda Rhimes

DATE:

Why People Are Like That Today:

....

....

....

....

....

....

....

....

....

....

....

....

TODAY'S DEFINITIVE CONCLUSION ABOUT HUMANITY:

☐   ☐   ☐   ☐

Man is such a fool

Why are we saving him?

Billie Eilish

DATE:

Why People Are Like That Today:

<!-- ruled writing lines -->

TODAY'S DEFINITIVE CONCLUSION ABOUT HUMANITY:

☐   ☐   ☐   ☐

People think it must be fun to be a super genius, but they don't realize how hard it is to put up with all the idiots in the world.

Bill Watterson

DATE:

Why People Are Like That Today:

....

....

....

....

....

....

....

....

....

....

....

....

TODAY'S DEFINITIVE CONCLUSION ABOUT HUMANITY:

☐   ☐   ☐   ☐

My coach said I run like a girl. And I said if he ran a little faster he could too.

Mia Hamm

Why People Are Like That Today:

....

....

....

....

....

....

....

....

....

....

....

....

TODAY'S DEFINITIVE CONCLUSION ABOUT HUMANITY:

☐   ☐   ☐   ☐

Cabbage, *n.* A familiar kitchen-garden vegetable about as large and wise as a man's head.

Ambrose Bierce

DATE:

Why People Are Like That Today:

....

....

....

....

....

....

....

....

....

....

....

....

....

....

....

TODAY'S DEFINITIVE CONCLUSION ABOUT HUMANITY:

☐   ☐   ☐   ☐

I personally think we developed language because of our deep inner need to complain.

Lily Tomlin

Why People Are Like That Today:

....

....

....

....

....

....

....

....

....

....

....

....

TODAY'S DEFINITIVE CONCLUSION ABOUT HUMANITY:

☐   ☐   ☐   ☐

When they discover the center of the universe, a lot of people will be disappointed to discover they are not it.

Bernard Bailey

DATE:

Why People Are Like That Today:

....

....

....

....

....

....

....

....

....

....

....

....

....

TODAY'S DEFINITIVE CONCLUSION ABOUT HUMANITY:

☐   ☐   ☐   ☐

Lord, what fools these mortals be!

William Shakespeare

DATE:

Why People Are Like That Today:

TODAY'S DEFINITIVE CONCLUSION ABOUT HUMANITY:

☐   ☐   ☐   ☐

There are only two or three human stories, and they go on repeating themselves as fiercely as if they had never happened before.

Willa Cather

DATE:

Why People Are Like That Today:

....

....

....

....

....

....

....

....

....

....

....

....

TODAY'S DEFINITIVE CONCLUSION ABOUT HUMANITY:

☐   ☐   ☐   ☐

There are two sides to every question: my side and the wrong side.

Oscar Levant

Why People Are Like That Today:

....

....

....

....

....

....

....

....

....

....

....

....

....

....

TODAY'S DEFINITIVE CONCLUSION ABOUT HUMANITY:

☐   ☐   ☐   ☐

God knows I've got so many frailties myself, I ought to be able to understand and forgive them in others. But I don't.

Ava Gardner

DATE:

Why People Are Like That Today:

....

....

....

....

....

....

....

....

....

....

....

....

....

....

TODAY'S DEFINITIVE CONCLUSION ABOUT HUMANITY:

☐   ☐   ☐   ☐

My loathings are simple: stupidity, oppression, crime, cruelty, soft music.

Vladimir Nabokov

Why People Are Like That Today:

....

....

....

....

....

....

....

....

....

....

....

....

....

....

....

TODAY'S DEFINITIVE CONCLUSION ABOUT HUMANITY:

☐   ☐   ☐   ☐

When dealing with people, let us remember we are not dealing with creatures of logic. We are dealing with creatures of emotion, creatures bristling with prejudices and motivated by pride and vanity.

Dale Carnegie

Why People Are Like That Today:

TODAY'S DEFINITIVE CONCLUSION ABOUT HUMANITY:

☐   ☐   ☐   ☐

Humanity I love you because when you're hard up you pawn your intelligence to buy a drink . . .

E. E. Cummings

Why People Are Like That Today:

TODAY'S DEFINITIVE CONCLUSION ABOUT HUMANITY:

☐   ☐   ☐   ☐

I am free of all prejudice. I hate everyone equally.

W. C. Fields

DATE:

Why People Are Like That Today:

....

....

....

....

....

....

....

....

....

....

....

....

TODAY'S DEFINITIVE CONCLUSION ABOUT HUMANITY:

☐   ☐   ☐   ☐

I am tired of living in a world where women are mostly referred to as a man's past, present, or future, property, or possession. I . . . do not belong to anyone but myself and neither do you.

Ariana Grande

DATE:

Why People Are Like That Today:

TODAY'S DEFINITIVE CONCLUSION ABOUT HUMANITY:

☐   ☐   ☐   ☐

Science may carry us to Mars, but it will leave the earth peopled as ever by the inept.

Agnes Repplier

DATE:

Why People Are Like That Today:

....

....

....

....

....

....

....

....

....

....

....

....

TODAY'S DEFINITIVE CONCLUSION ABOUT HUMANITY:

☐ 　　☐ 　　☐ 　　☐

I regard you with an indifference closely bordering on aversion.

Robert Louis Stevenson

DATE:

Why People Are Like That Today:

....

....

....

....

....

....

....

....

....

....

TODAY'S DEFINITIVE CONCLUSION ABOUT HUMANITY:

☐ 　　☐ 　　☐ 　　☐

The good Earth— we could have saved it, but we were too damn cheap and lazy.

Kurt Vonnegut

DATE:

Why People Are Like That Today:

....

....

....

....

....

....

....

....

....

....

....

....

TODAY'S DEFINITIVE CONCLUSION ABOUT HUMANITY:

☐   ☐   ☐   ☐

Happiness in intelligent people is the rarest thing I know.

Ernest Hemingway

DATE:

Why People Are Like That Today:

....

....

....

....

....

....

....

....

....

....

....

....

....

....

TODAY'S DEFINITIVE CONCLUSION ABOUT HUMANITY:

☐   ☐   ☐   ☐

I don't dislike babies, though I think very young ones rather disgusting.

Queen Victoria

DATE:

Why People Are Like That Today:

....

....

....

....

....

....

....

....

....

....

....

....

TODAY'S DEFINITIVE CONCLUSION ABOUT HUMANITY:

☐   ☐   ☐   ☐

I like long walks, especially when they are taken by people who annoy me.

Fred Allen

DATE:

Why People Are Like That Today:

....

....

....

....

....

....

....

....

....

....

....

....

....

....

TODAY'S DEFINITIVE CONCLUSION ABOUT HUMANITY:

☐   ☐   ☐   ☐

I have never killed anyone, but I have read some obituary notices with great satisfaction.

Clarence Darrow

DATE:

Why People Are Like That Today:

....
....
....
....
....
....
....
....
....
....
....
....
....

TODAY'S DEFINITIVE CONCLUSION ABOUT HUMANITY:

☐   ☐   ☐   ☐

The world is a botched job.

Gabriel García Márquez

Why People Are Like That Today:

TODAY'S DEFINITIVE CONCLUSION ABOUT HUMANITY:

I've always been interested in people, but I've never liked them.

W. Somerset Maugham

DATE:

Why People Are Like That Today:

....

....

....

....

....

....

....

....

....

....

....

....

....

TODAY'S DEFINITIVE CONCLUSION ABOUT HUMANITY:

☐   ☐   ☐   ☐

We are all worms. But I do believe that I am a glow-worm.

Winston Churchill

DATE:

Why People Are Like That Today:

....

....

....

....

....

....

....

....

....

....

....

....

TODAY'S DEFINITIVE CONCLUSION ABOUT HUMANITY:

☐   ☐   ☐   ☐

Just because you're paranoid don't mean they're not after you.

Kurt Cobain

Why People Are Like That Today:

TODAY'S DEFINITIVE CONCLUSION ABOUT HUMANITY:

☐ 　☐ 　☐ 　☐

I hate being high-fived. Do I look like the kind of girl that likes to be high-fived?

Dita Von Teese

DATE:

Why People Are Like That Today:

....

....

....

....

....

....

....

....

....

....

TODAY'S DEFINITIVE CONCLUSION ABOUT HUMANITY:

☐ 　　☐ 　　☐ 　　☐

There are few people whom I really love, and still fewer of whom I think well. The more I see of the world, the more am I dissatisfied with it.

Jane Austen

DATE:

Why People Are Like That Today:

TODAY'S DEFINITIVE CONCLUSION ABOUT HUMANITY:

I prefer rogues to imbeciles, because they sometimes take a rest.

Alexandre Dumas Père

DATE:

Why People Are Like That Today:

....

....

....

....

....

....

....

....

....

....

....

TODAY'S DEFINITIVE CONCLUSION ABOUT HUMANITY:

☐   ☐   ☐   ☐

It's hard to be humble when you're as great as I am.

Muhammad Ali